THE UNIFIED WALLET

Kyle J. J. Kemper

i

Published by Peacock Books

For more information on how to work with us, visit PeacockBooks.co

eBook Edition ISBN: 978-1-9994480-3-5

Paperback Edition ISBN: 978-1-9994480-2-8

Contents

About The Author

Kyle James Joachim Kemper is a problem-solving Canadian tech/crypto expert. He is a visionary, a connector, and an artist. He has traveled the world, observing, learning, and sharing knowledge with people from all walks of life. He educates and inspires people to be positive, proactive, and passionate. His journey follows many industries including venture capital, app development, construction, serving, marketing, communications, events, and blockchain technology.

Since 2013, Kyle has accumulated more than fifteen thousand hours in blockchain experience, having worked with and advised numerous companies within the ecosystem.

A firm believer in love, liberty, and honourable value creation, Kyle J J Kemper seeks to have a positive impact on the world and is relentless in his drive to bring about positive social change. He cherishes the opportunity to learn, listen, and help others, so don't hesitate to connect with him @kylekemper on Twitter. If you would like to support Kyle on his journey, consider becoming a patron at http://patreon.com/kjjk

Foreword

I remember my first wallet. I made it from a kit, with pieces of leather stitched together to construct a billfold, a change purse, and a sleeve to carry a card or a neatly creased paper form, such as a library card or driver's licence (I wasn't yet old enough to drive). My homemade wallet was more than the sum of its parts. It was my independence, my conduit to freedom in society, and my transition to full personhood. Over the years, I've had countless wallets: I've lost them, had them returned, and fully drenched them in a canoe upset, but I never remember being far from home without one. While my wallet's not actually me, it's always been a part of me.

We are now evolving beyond leather into the realm of digital wallets. Our phones and the services enabling our phones are becoming our wallets beyond the leather kind. Only now are we beginning to realize the vast, transformative powers that this new breed of wallets hold. Kyle Kemper, in his book, provides us with a solid foundation of a digital wallet, pushing the concept one step beyond the traditional horizon to a unified digital wallet. Kyle has written a personal and compelling account of how the unified digital wallet will become no less than our digital selves, our trusted, ubiquitous instruments of agency embedded into our personal and professional lives and into the extended lives of our devices, our services, and our avatars existing at our behest within our digital realms.

Kyle provides us with a clear and present glimpse of the next big thing—the unified digital wallet stewarding our assets, managing our relationships, and expressing the essence of our digital identity. As Marco Polo returned from his journeys on the Silk Road, converting his fortunes to gemstones, Kyle takes us on a captivating journey of the leather wallet evolving and transforming into a unified digital wallet to become the most important thing that we as digital citizens will have to conduct our affairs in every aspect of our digital lives.

In closing, I entreat you to read Kyle's book. Enter the realm of the unified digital wallet. It will change you. It will change us all.

Tim Bouma, Senior Analyst, Digital Identity
Government of Canada

Chapter 1

Why we Need a Digital Wallet

We have a physical wallet where we store combinations of cash, plastic cards, receipts, and other things. We also have phones. What if we could securely put everything into a secure digital wallet accessible on our phone? This digitization is happening now and we're just at the tipping point.

Digitization is fundamentally changing what a wallet is and what a wallet can do. On the most basic level, it is revolutionizing how we pay for things. We use plastic cards for payments; physical objects that connect to our bank accounts or creditors and authorize access. We'll be able to use dynamic digital cards that replace the pieces of plastic in our wallet. A digital, secure, location aware keychain capable of a wide variety of functions. Payments, Identity, Currency, Contracts, Loyalty, Social...the list goes on.

A physical wallet is spatially limited. Everyone has experienced their wallet becoming cluttered with too many cards and too many receipts. We carry around the loyalty card to the coffee shop that we rarely go to on the off chance that we happen to stop by. But there is only so much we can carry around with us, so we have to be selective about what we put there.

This is not an issue for digital wallets. With a digital wallet, we can store as many cards as we like. There's simply no limit to the amount of content that we can have there. Instead of making choices based on spatial limitations, this technology creates new opportunities for integration and connectivity. It will allow for simplified consumer experiences, the creation of new marketing approaches, and permit interactions between programs and services that were once separate.

To store, send, receive, and request digital assets, we need to have a digital wallet. Digital assets are known alternatively as digital or virtual currencies and most popularly as cryptocurrencies. Bitcoin, Ethereum, Ripple, Litecoin, Dogecoin, and a plethora of other cryptocurrencies are now active mediums of exchange, and these "cryptos" will only proliferate as technology becomes a more normal part of the ordinary consumer's experience.

Blockchain is the basis of all digital currency technology. Blockchain is a continually growing list of transaction records, a digital ledger that ensures the authenticity of an individual unit of asset by recording its history of ownership back to its creation. Every digital currency has its own blockchain, and, consequently, every digital currency requires its own associated digital wallet for users to manage their tokens. If we want to own and store different digital currencies, we need to have many wallets.

This complicates the user experience and limits the potential for digital wallets to replace physical ones. The issue is that there is a great need for a comprehensive digital wallet in an increasingly digital world. As more and more services go online, we need a way to make purchases, provide identification, and secure our personal information. We need to move from a world of passwords to a world of keys.

Passwords are ubiquitous to our online experience. We have a password to access our email, a different one to access our online banking, and many more to log on to discussion forums, streaming services, and retail sites. Or, we should have a different password for all these things. In practice, many people have terrible password practices. They reuse passwords, pick obvious ones, and have to write them down to remember.

Passwords are insecure. If we use the same password over and over again to access different sites and services, it becomes easier for a malicious actor to gain control of our information and defraud us through social engineering. This is why it is important to move away from passwords and protect our information with digital keys instead.

Digital keys are a more sophisticated kind of password. They are much longer than typical passwords and are created by a program rather than by a user. A key is a cryptographic signature that allows us to establish true authenticity over whatever claim we have.

In the case of cryptocurrencies, keys are essential to spending and moving these assets around. There are public keys and private keys. The public key is like an email address or an account number. It is how we are identified in the system for the transfer of assets. The private key is like the password to our email account, only far more secure. It's what allows us to control our wallet and assets.

But a key is not something we are capable of remembering. They're not based on our mother's birthday. They're not reusable across different services. They appear as long strings of letters and numbers, essentially chosen at random but entirely unique across a given system.

For this reason, there needs to be a secure way to manage our keys. It would be impractical to write down the key and lock it away in a safe. It cannot simply be stored on a physical system that could be lost or hacked, and there is currently no effective digital system for managing and accessing the various keys needed to navigate different secure services in one place.

This is the most important function that an open digital wallet can provide. As we move toward a truly connected environment, a master key will be needed to unlock services, products, and experiences. Unlocking this master key will require some kind of secure authentication, such as a PIN, fingerprint, faceID, or some emerging biometric. Storing keys in a secure digital wallet is essential to implementing secure technology in a user-friendly way.

A digital wallet is effectively a place to hold all our information. It's our personal black box. Think about the way a black box works on a plane. It records all the information about the flight, what's happening at any given moment, where it is, and contains its maintenance records.

The same is true for our digital wallet. It is a record of all our transactions. It can hold all our receipts in digitized form. It holds access to our digital monies and assets. It holds our digital titles and property records, our digital identity documents, and anything else that we might store in a physical wallet. It's exactly like the wallet in our pocket, accessible through our phone or other device.

This will allow for a seamless user experience not only in commerce but also in healthcare, wills, and other applications.

To understand what this means, let us imagine what our current, non-seamless experience is like regarding commerce. When I go to pay for something today, I must pull out my wallet and produce a plastic card. I usually need to go to a point of sale terminal, where I enter a PIN, and then I get a piece of paper representing my receipt, which I have to hold onto to signify my ownership and, potentially, for return or exchange purposes. If I lose the receipt or throw it away, it becomes more difficult to engage in any of these post-purchase activities.

By contrast, the seamless experience of a digital wallet allows for a much easier interaction with a merchant or service provider. A digital wallet permits access to all our payment options, meaning that we can make purchases using either traditional currencies, credit, or cryptocurrencies. It automatically collects and stores our digital receipt. It will connect us to the store's loyalty program and to automatically apply to new loyalty programs through selective sharing of relevant information. It will also streamline the retail experience in other ways for the benefit of consumers and merchants alike.

This will have significant implications for more complicated retail experiences. Assume, for example, that you wear prescription glasses and need to replace them either because they've been lost or damaged or you have a new prescription. With a digital wallet that includes our most recent prescription, face measurements, address, and payment method, we could select the frames we want online and have them shipped to us with a single click.

Or imagine that we're going to a nightclub. At most clubs these days everyone is asked to show their ID.

We walk up to the front door and the bouncer demands to see our IDs. When we give them our driver's licence or whatever else, we're actually giving them a lot more information than they really need. Their job is to confirm we are over an age-limit so they are not liable. When we give them our driver's licence they get to see our full legal names, home addresses, date of birth and more.

A digital wallet would seamlessly allow for a more selective sharing of information. We would merely need to pass the bouncer verified proofs of age along with a verified photo, reducing our exposure in terms of the information we are sharing that is not relevant to the interaction. The same principle can apply to other information exchanges, with digital wallets providing a straightforward means of releasing relevant information while securing unnecessary information.

Consider what happens when we are pulled over by a police officer while driving. We have to provide our driver's licence, insurance, and registration, all of which had better be with us or we could face additional penalties. A digital wallet can hold all this information and allow us to share it with an officer on their recorded request. A digital ticket can be issued which we could immediately pay or file a dispute.

For the ordinary person, using this technology will greatly simplify all kinds of everyday interactions, commercial or otherwise. Instead of fumbling through a physical wallet for the right payment option, remembering several unique PINs and passwords, holding onto a printed receipt, and producing different documents for identification purposes, the digital wallet will securely collect all these tools and information in one place. It will store our proof of purchase along with warranty and title information. It will also provide a mechanism to give instant feedback to the merchant through ranking or commenting communications.

This will lead to a better consumer experience as this technology is more widely adopted. Digital wallets will remove friction points from various commercial, medical, legal, and other experiences. They will make digital currency more usable in a wider set of circumstances and reduce many costs and associated fees of transactions, making the entire economy more efficient.

This technology will revolutionize the way we conduct our affairs and how we engage with the world around us. The blockchain revolution is happening, but it remains fragmented between different services, cryptocurrencies, and distinct applications. An open digital wallet is the way to move ahead, making this technology more integrated and easier to use. What is needed now is a considered, authoritative stance on what the open digital wallet can look like, what this technology must provide to make this future our reality, and how stakeholders from all over the world can come together to create it.

Chapter 2

Cryptocurrencies, Digital Assets, and the Future of Blockchain

Bitcoin proved that we could securely store digital assets by ourselves without the need for a centralized governing body. It created a digital file called a blockchain that cannot be altered as opposed to the easily replicable file formats we use for digitized music, video, or text documents. Bitcoin solved the problem of how we can have digital assets that can't be easily duplicated through a copy and paste function, and it accomplished this through blockchain technology.

Bitcoin was released by Satoshi Nakamoto in 2009, and since that time, it has been growing, adopted, and accepted by greater numbers of people than could have possibly been expected. The network has grown stronger, with great potential to replace national currencies for many kinds of transactions.

The way Bitcoin works is through blockchain. Think about the first bank account that you ever had. My first bank account came with a little blue bank book—a ledger in which I would record the deposits and withdrawals to keep track of when I was withdrawing and depositing money. I would have my own personal ledger, and the bank would keep a duplicate ledger. All across the world, banks,

accountants, lawyers, and bank customers are all
keeping little ledgers of data that they could verify
as true so long as they accorded with everyone
else's ledger of the same account.

What Satoshi figured out with Bitcoin was a way to
have a shared ledger that everybody who used the
currency could see. Everybody has access to the
same ledger, which is updated at regular intervals,
approximately every ten minutes in the case of
Bitcoin. These updates show the entire network
what transactions have taken place and the
addresses in possession of each unique coin.

This is the essence of blockchain—a distributed
ledger technology that consists of a constantly
updated master file. It is not possible to
retroactively alter the file to hide or distort past
transactions because it's open and shared among all
users in the world. There are measures to ensure
that the information on the blockchain is public or
private. Bitcoin, the first blockchain, is a public
blockchain where all transactions are viewable and
verifiable.

With Bitcoin, we hold keys that control tokens on
the network, accessible using a digital wallet. The
tokens are registered on the blockchain and
attributed to a public address/key that can be
verified by anyone if they know our address. To
spend or transfer our tokens, we need the private
key to move the Bitcoin to someone else's address.
Once we send someone the Bitcoin, nothing can be

10

done to undo the transaction. There's no governing authority that can reverse it, and it can't be spent again. This makes it easy, fast, and secure. Think of it as digital cash.

Cryptocurrencies, such as Bitcoin, make use of digital wallets to store private keys, but while they are called digital wallets, they are more like digital money clips. We haven't reached the full potential for this technology. Right now, there are many different types of digital wallets. Some support one currency, some support several different currencies, and others have unique functions tied to services.

To understand the challenge, let me explain my current situation. On my phone, I have Edge Wallet (Bitcoin, Ethereum, Bitcoin Cash, Litecoin, Dash, Monero, and more), Bread Wallet (Bitcoin), Blockchain Wallet (Bitcoin, Bitcoin Cash, Ethereum), Copay (Bitcoin, Bitcoin Cash, Multi-signature support), Loaf Wallet (Litecoin), Dash Wallet (DASH), Jaxx (many currencies), Coinomi (many currencies), Doge Wallet (Dogecoin!), Steem, Sweatcoin, Datawallet . . . and that is just wallets. Then there are apps for exchanges and crypto banks, such as Coinbase, Coinberry, Coinsquare, and Kraken. I use an app called Earn that pays me Bitcoin for participating in surveys that are relevant to me. Essentially, I have small amounts of crypto all over the place, which is a hassle. So many wallets and disparate services may work for me but it's simply not accessible for my mother or the average Instagram user.

Kyle Kemper

This means they aren't really wallets in that they don't replace the many functions of a physical wallet. They're digital money clips. These apps generally allow us to store, send, and receive cryptocurrencies while also keeping a history of transactions. They generally do not allow us to store ID cards, loyalty cards, bank cards, certifications, receipts, contact information, or other things we may have in our physical wallet.

In the future, many blockchains will be available for different uses and industries. They can be very large files that hold vast amounts of data. The digital wallets don't keep full copies of the blockchain. The blockchain files are stored on storage networks around the world. What the wallet holds are the keys, the secure access codes that are required to access the digital assets and can then trigger transactions on the given blockchain.

The blockchain revolution is being touted as the the fourth industrial revolution, but where I become frustrated is at the user experience level. We have genius engineers and visionaries developing solutions for all industries to alleviate friction points, but a gap exists when it comes to basic use. Enter the gamers.

A comprehensive, standardized, open-sourced, global consortia guided digital wallet can become this wallet that unlocks the blockchain revolution and brings identity and financial services to billions. A golden age of civilization. A platform for digital wallet apps that provides additional services and interactions with these blockchains and their correlated services. This can include identification, titles, certifications, and the like. Currently, we have to visit many different websites, we need physical cards, and sometimes we must appear in person to deal with tellers or service agents to accomplish these functions, but it is possible to interact with all of these from a digital wallet.

Holding keys in our digital wallet is like holding bank cards in our physical wallet. A bank card does not physically hold our assets but rather links to an account that we can access to make payments or transfers. The difference with cryptocurrencies is that there are no banks. There's a network with open access to the blockchain that is accountable to everyone. In terms of software, all we need to access this network and trade in this currency is a place to store our digital keys.

From a user perspective, a wallet allows us to access and review our digital assets. It's where we go to see how much of a balance we have in a given cryptocurrency. It's the tool we use to send some of our assets to another address or request a payment from another user. It is like a mailbox for money that allows us to seamlessly make exchanges with anyone, anywhere in the world.

There are many different digital wallets in the current environment. This is limiting the potential of blockchain technology. Imagine if we had to have one physical wallet to shop at the grocery store and a different one for the coffee shop or if we had to keep our dollars in one place and our euros in another when we're going back and forth between the two. It slows down our ability to make transactions and makes it more complicated to know what types of assets we have in our possession at any given time.

Now think about loyalty cards. We have a card to collect loyalty points, a physical card that is connected to an account that contains a virtual currency offered in exchange for personal information. When we go to the particular store that has this loyalty program, we must produce our physical card or else have an app loaded on our phone. It's a haphazard system. Maybe we forgot the card, maybe it's too much effort to find it when we have bags of groceries in front of we. And these systems may not even be secure. They're likely to use a username and password system rather than blockchain backed by digital keys.

A comprehensive digital wallet built on blockchain can collect all these services into one easy-to-use platform. It can manage our cryptocurrencies and traditional bank accounts. It can connect our loyalty programs to our payment options. It can contain digitized versions of health cards, driver's licences, CAA membership, insurance, and any number of similar services. And blockchain will allow all this information to be securely stored in one place while granting considerable control over what information we share and when.

Blockchain and digital identity has made it possible to create decentralized, secure currency exchange platforms. The next stage of the blockchain revolution will be the extension of this decentralized security to a streamlined user experience. A comprehensive digital wallet built on blockchain is one way to move this technology ahead and bring about a massive wave of adoption.

Chapter 3

Wallet vs. Phone

The transition from physical to digital wallets will change the most fundamental ways that we interact with others in our economy, but we will still require some means of accessing our digital wallets, some device to facilitate our purchases and transactions. Smartphones are a nearly ubiquitous technology that enables such actions, but we are only beginning to see their potential to revolutionize commerce. For this reason, it is important to understand the difference between a wallet and a phone.

A wallet is generally static. A physical wallet is just a device that holds and organizes information. This information comes in the form of bank and credit cards, identification, loyalty and membership cards, cash, and quite often receipts.

Some of the most advanced physical wallets incorporate some level of technology. I have one, for example, that protects the contents from RFID scanners, but there is only so much that can be done to innovate the physical wallet. There might be a better design to foster better organization. There might be other possible security measures, but its core function of holding these materials for we to carry around is basically set.

The biggest limitation of physical wallets is that while they can store cards they don't allow for those cards to talk to each other. It's not possible for our Shoppers Optimum card to run a cross-promotion with our Air Miles card. Nor is it possible for our credit card to confirm our age when we make a purchase at the liquor store. This is why physical wallets are static. As a platform, they have no potential to integrate the information stored within.

A phone, by contrast, is an open and dynamic platform. A phone has an Internet connection. It has a camera, which means it also has a scanner. It has a keyboard. It has a programmable operating system that can be customized with apps, and it has fingerprint touch ID biometrics, which can be a useful security measure.

This open and dynamic platform creates a world of potential concerning what phones can do. Phones can already do a lot more than a physical wallet can, and there is endless potential to innovate them both as devices and as platforms for other applications.

Most intriguing, phones can duplicate many of the functions of our physical wallets. This is already happening to some extent as banking and credit card services create apps that replicate the purchasing functions of cards. It is happening with cryptocurrencies, which have apps that connect to their digital wallets.

I've purchased jewelry on Venice Beach using Bitcoin and my phone, plane tickets from Cheapair.com, conference tickets, and beer on the beach in Rincon, Puerto Rico. Phone-based commerce is easy and secure, and we're only going to see more of it as people get used to the technology.

Even with our phone, however, the challenge is that these apps and services aren't talking to each other. In that way, it's the same as a physical wallet. There are still very limited interoperability functions. So if we have an app for a loyalty program, we still need to verify our identity with a physical driver's licence. Right now, we need both a wallet and a phone, and we need to know what information is where and create manual connections.

But a lot more will be possible once we have everything stored in a centralized, self-sovereign digital wallet. Self-sovereign means you own your data. You are in control of your assets. You are the king/queen of your kingdom.

There are certainly concerns about concentrating all this information in a single place. We could lose our phone, or the device could be compromised, but physical wallets can be lost or stolen also, and if our wallet is stolen, there's very little that can be done to protect its contents. We can cancel our credit cards and issue new IDs at some expense, but any cash we had is likely gone forever.

Moving this information to a digital wallet accessible from our phones provides additional security. Phones can be safeguarded by passwords and biometrics, and a phone does not carry cryptocurrency in the way that a physical wallet carries cash. It is a means of accessing something stored securely on blockchains around the world.

With a digital wallet assuming the functions of a physical wallet, it becomes much more secure. All wallet data can be stored in the cloud in an encrypted file. This file is then downloaded to our wallet app on whatever device, and we merely authenticate our identity to unlock the contents of the wallet. This means we will no longer be exposed to the risks of losing our phone or our wallet. All our data will forever be accessible.

Digital wallets will allow us to perform the same function as a physical wallet through our phone, but interoperability will make the user experience faster and better, as we'll always have access to our cards, identification, and information. we'll be able to control how much information we release for any interaction, making it more secure than handing over our driver's licence with our home address to the nightclub bouncers.

This digital wallet format makes it possible to selectively share only the information that is required by another party, something a physical wallet can only dream about. Because a mobile device is location-aware, it can facilitate a concept called geofencing, which is the idea that our phone can be triggered to perform a certain action when we enter a particular physical space. At a retail location, we could be standing in line for the cashier and our phone could detect that and streamline the purchase experience. It could request access to our loyalty program. It could inform us of the payment amount and our payment options. It could ask us to provide feedback on our shopping experience, the cleanliness of the store, or the quality of the product and service offerings.

At some point, we may not even need to stand in line to interact with a cashier at all. We could just take our purchases to the checkout area, where they are scanned, and we take care of the entire transaction over our phones.

This streamlined user experience will create new opportunities for businesses as well. Perhaps we have a delicious meal at a restaurant. As we are paying on our phone, we could be prompted to write a Yelp review. It's possible to even incentivize this behaviour in the form of a discount or an ongoing loyalty program. This could be similar to the Uber feedback system, where we give a star rating and there is a guided experience to provide additional qualitative feedback.

Streamlining data collection in these ways creates an incredibly efficient experience for both businesses and users. When we have a really good experience at a restaurant or a store, we want to tell people about it. We want to compliment the chef, but we also want it to be easy to do. Right now only a small subset of people are leaving restaurant reviews, and that can skew the data in significant ways. Storing all our keys to the multitude of services we use in our digital wallet will enable these kinds of connections and make everything more streamlined.

A unified digital wallet will empower users to make transactions with the ease of using a phone. Rather than searching through a cumbersome, static wallet for the right card for the right situation, everything will be stored in the same place. It will allow for easy interaction between different accounts and services, and it will be far more secure than a physical wallet because it will all be backed up in the secure cloud.

In time, we will look back at physical wallets the same way we look at typewriters. They will be artifacts of a particular time and place, and we will be amazed that we used to carry around such sensitive information in our back pockets, where it could be lost, stolen, or overshared.

Chapter 4

From Physical Wallets to Digital

Unlike their physical counterparts, digital wallets will offer unlimited storage capacity. we will be able to put every card in our wallet, and it will have no perceptible effect in our pocket. Imagine never losing a card or imagine being able to pull up the loyalty card from the coffee shop we visited in a distant city if we pass that way again! That's a very powerful function that cannot be achieved with a physical wallet.

Currently, digital wallets are exclusively used for managing digital assets. They allow users to store, send, receive, and request cryptocurrencies, and each cryptocurrency tends to have its own specific digital wallets.

Integrating all these cryptocurrencies into a single wallet will greatly simplify the user experience of making transactions with digital assets, which will be increasingly important with the proliferation of types of cryptocurrency and blockchain-backed services.

Cryptocurrencies will become increasingly popular because they represent choice. They are open source by design and cannot be counterfeited or re-created. This makes them more secure than traditional bank notes, which can be forged, albeit with some difficulty.

The value of a cryptocurrency is determined by its market and the utility it provides. There's been a lot of competition and innovation recently around digital currencies, and there is every reason to believe this trend will continue because cryptocurrencies give people choice in a way that traditional currencies do not. Different cryptos can fulfil different functions and utilities. They can be global money, such as Bitcoin or Ethereum, or there can be loyalty currencies that only work at specific retailers or for specific purchases.

People will need to manage different digital currencies. I do not believe that one cryptocurrency will dominate all areas of commerce. We are entering the era of currency choice.

Instead of being forced to use centrally issued currencies, digital currencies permit consumers and retailers to choose the most appropriate medium of exchange for their transaction. Digital wallets are already capable of managing digital currencies. The next step will be to integrate the other functions of the physical wallet to deliver unparalleled payment, retail, and social experiences.

What will this transition look like? From a user perspective, I see a simple process of digitizing the existing contents of one's physical wallet.

23

Kyle Kemper

The camera and optical image recognition software on our smartphones can facilitate this information capture, backup, and upload. A unified digital wallet could allow us to take photos of all our existing cards, detecting the pertinent information contained therein. This will immediately create a digital backup of that physical card. It could then seamlessly integrate this information into the digital wallet and install the associated app/extension for whatever service that card represents.

For example, once we scan our Air Miles card to this digital wallet, we'll have a persistent digital backup that can be credited anywhere we can collect Air Miles points. Without a digital wallet, we have to pull out the card and scan it. With the digital wallet, we won't need to do anything. Anytime we make a purchase, the wallet would simply see whether or not there is an Air Miles request and if so the data would be passed instantly.

Then there is the information that we generally do not carry around with us in a physical wallet. There are assets that are too valuable to trust to the relative insecurity of a physical wallet. We wouldn't carry around all our assets in cash in our back pocket, and there are other assets, such as cars, televisions, and houses that are not portable. But we do have documentation to prove that we own them.

Think about a valuable asset, such as a university degree. For the most part, we don't need to prove to people that we have a degree. Maybe we have a

24

framed certificate hanging in our home or office, but if we do need to prove it, we have to contact our institution and go through a process to retrieve our transcripts or certification. We're not going to carry a degree around in our physical wallet. With a digital wallet, however, we could have this information at our fingertips. The same is true for proof of ownership for titles and deeds for our most valuable assets. There's no limit to how much information we could store in a digital wallet, and this goes far beyond the cards and currency we carry with us every day.

Maybe we want to take out a loan. Any reputable lender will ask us to provide some collateral, which requires access to titles or comparable information. With a digital wallet, we could have all that documentation readily available in a way that would streamline the entire process of applying for a loan.

In some ways, it would be similar to the traditional wallet. When we buy a physical wallet, it comes empty. we decide what cards we want in it, how they are arranged, whether or not we have a photo of our children in it, or whatever we decide to carry in our physical wallet. It's the same with a phone. A smartphone comes loaded with basic functions, but it's up to us to customize it by downloading apps that allow for different functionalities. If we don't use Twitter, we don't need the app for it. If we want Uber, we have to select it.

This is how a unified digital wallet should operate in my humble opinion. Most current digital wallets do not allow us to add extensible apps to perform different functions. We're talking about simple apps that allow us to manage different digital currencies through the same program. There can be smart apps for all sorts of functions. Apps for accounting. Apps for estate planning and wills. Apps/games for trading and using kitten-themed rare trading cards. Survey apps. Loyalty apps. Voting apps. Insurance apps. Betting apps. Getting the picture? . . . wallet apps.

This unified digital wallet will allow us to manage assets across platforms and apps. It will allow for the creation of new apps that manage these assets within the digital wallet system. There will be apps that secure our identification, which would only reveal pertinent information needed for any interaction. There will be apps for retail loyalty programs and apps for traditional banking and credit card institutions.

There are apps that do many of these things already. The difference would be that the digital wallet allows for these programs to securely interact with one another. The digital wallet will be a repository for the keys that we need to access the programs and services that characterize modern commerce. It is about bringing all these things together into a single interface that will be easy to use and foster collaborative benefits and interactions.

Making a successful transition from physical wallets to digital ones will require a non-proprietary approach . . . a unified approach.

The digital wallet should be highly extendable to the needs of users. What is needed is an open platform that encourages innovation in app development, user experience, interconnectivity, and community empowerment.

And it must be interoperable across platforms. For example, digital wallets need to operate on iPhone, Android, Windows, and Blackberry. They need to be accessible through other devices, e.g., on laptops, tablets, and whatever else emerges in the years to come. It will need to be compatible with VR because virtual reality is here. It's becoming mainstream, and we're going to need access to our wallets when playing high-stakes poker in deep space.

The digital wallet can be a portal to our digital self. It is both our briefcase and our safe, something we can take everywhere and trust that its contents are secure. It will be our personal black box. It will supplant the functionalities of the physical wallet and interconnect the services on our phone as we've never seen before.

People are already treating their phones as digital wallets. There are apps connecting to bank accounts and credit cards that allow us to pay by scanning our phone. Cryptocurrency wallets allow transactions between users. People are increasingly taking photos of the cards in their wallets as a backup just in case they lose them. This is like a hack into making a digital wallet, but it is a poor substitute for a unified digital wallet because it is no more secure than our photo gallery.

A digital wallet will fulfil these capabilities while being much more secure. Not only more secure than storing personal information in our phone's photo gallery, but also more secure than a physical wallet. At some point in the future people will question whether there is even a need to carry a physical wallet at all? Why will we need to carry around these pieces of plastic when we have all the information on our phone? Battery life and connectivity are near term reasons but as we see infinite battery life and global wireless access on the horizon they will likely be addressed. But one of the greatest reasons to move to a digital wallet is security.

If our physical wallet is stolen, our cards are gone. Their information is backed up with the institutions that issued them, be they banks for credit and debit cards or government agencies for identification. A digital wallet will have all this information stored in the cloud, where we can access it from any device if our phone goes missing. Instead of a cumbersome process of contacting every institution for replacements, it will be as simple as verifying our identity on any device.

In my heart, I feel as though society is ready to transition from constraining physical systems to open digital alternatives. The digital wallet is a harbinger for this kind of transformation. Digital wallets will end limitations on storage capacity, make managing many different kinds of digital assets easy, and allow us to backup and store personal information with greater control and greater security.

The transition to digital wallets will completely revolutionize the most basic ways we interact in our economy, and the possibilities are limitless for the direction that users and developers will take this technology. The future is very exciting!

Chapter 5

Open-Source Everything

Open-source is a term that is thrown around a lot when we talk generally about the openness of digital platforms, but, of course, it has a technical meaning. Open source means that the code of the software is available for everybody to see, discuss, and modify. This is to verify everything that's going on with it as well as make it easier to develop complementary programs and create extensible applications.

Open source design is important for maximizing the potential of the digital wallet. It's equivalent to the idea that when we buy a physical wallet at the store we are free to customize it however we want. We choose what goes into the wallet and what doesn't.

This is how the digital wallet should operate. If we want to store bitcoin in it, just add the bitcoin app to the wallet. Maybe we drive a car? we can choose to download a licence app to securely manage our government identification, likely offered by the government itself.

If someone has the coding skills, they can build an app to do all sorts of things. The key is that the digital wallet must be free and open to these kinds of innovations.

What if we create a new digital currency and want people to be able to buy and sell that currency through their digital wallets. What is this going to look like? Currently, three channels are available for distributing services to mobile devices.

The first is to build a website that supports mobile browsers. We all know how these sites work, but they're generally not as clean as the app. Think about Facebook via our mobile browser vs. Facebook via the app; a big difference!

Then there is Apple and its App Store, which is a private closed environment. This means that if we make an app we have to ask Apple's permission to put our app into their store. This limits the speed and diversity of innovation because of this effective governing authority that regulates this market. Many digital currency apps have struggled to get their apps listed because Apple enjoys and maintains a complete monopoly over app-level payments and can use their centralized authority to say no to solution providers who threaten their castle.

Another model is the Android platform, where users can freely install apps from any developer. Android also features app stores where there are certain requirements that any app must meet to be listed. What this means is that developers can test, use, and interact with their communities without going through gatekeepers. We can have private solutions to identified problems and build systems that are highly responsive to their users needs.

An open approach is essential for digital wallets. Everybody ought to be able to develop apps for this service, which could be easily installed through a QR Code, geofence push notification, or some kind of wallet app store. To assure quality, there can be certain verified information or basic requirements for these apps as with the Android store. There can be verified developers or services so that people have more information to judge the quality and security of a given app, but the open source approach is essential for unlocking the transformational potential of this technology.

For the base wallet system, an open source approach is essential for pairing with the development of new standards. This will allow everyone to see how the keys are stored, how the authentication works, and how data sharing and external communications function. This must be open source, validated, and audited by security providers and specialists.

Closed source programming is generally less secure than open source. It affords malicious actors the ability to exploit backdoors and hack systems to undermine their security. The sensitivity of the information being stored in the digital wallet is so great that closed source should never be used for the wallet itself. People need to be able to see how the system works if they are going to trust it with their assets and personal information.

The benefit of open source is that it is extensible. Users and developers can create applications for the system that its original designers might never have imagined. Think about the potential of a phone and location awareness. We could go into the checkout at a store and the watch notifies us to download the wallet app for that brands loyalty program. It could call up our passport information when we enter a country. A map when we enter a new city. It could pay the toll as we drive on the highway. There are so many little services that a digital wallet could provide where it can display some information or generate a new key, and all this will be possible through open application programming interfaces or APIs.

Open APIs allow anyone to develop apps for a platform. Banks can build apps that interact with the wallet just as they build apps for mobile phones. A digital wallet will ease the connections to other services, such as loyalty programs. A truly open and widely adopted base ecosystem offers developers the ability to build for the world. They can attain a critical mass of interest by simply innovating on the foundations. They can make apps dynamic and personal, or rigid and communal. Businesses and traditional digital service providers will want to be part of the system, and once a tipping point has been reached in terms of adoption they will all connect their offering to the unified wallet.

The other benefit is personalization. One of the great things about physical wallets is that they allow for a lot of personalization not only in terms of what we choose to put into them but also in terms of what they are as a physical object. We can choose the material, design, and style of our physical wallet. Many people want a leather wallet. Some people want a big wallet, while others prefer a small one. I like my wallet, but someone else may not necessarily feel the same. Everyone wants their own customizable user experience, and with so many different kinds of physical wallets in the world everyone can have it.

The same should apply to digital wallets. Open source user interface designs can make the wallets customizable and personal. Many designers are capable of working on skins and interfaces to deliver a certain type of user experience. All digital wallets can fulfil the same set of standard functions and be dressed up in a way that appeals to us individually. Chanel, Prada, Diesel, Hermes, Under Armor...all these brands could choose to offer a customized skin to give our wallet a familiar feel.

Such personalization can be more than just cosmetic. There is great potential for meaningful design innovations. Wearables and smart cards are giving people new tools to play with to develop new interfaces. New solutions, such as VR solutions, could be built upon the core wallet program to trigger all manner of new interactions with these different environments.

If we have a Fitbit, for example, there's the potential to connect it through APIs to our wallet so that it could act as a fob to enter our apartment after our run. There could be an additional app on top of that connecting our physical fitness data to our medical records.

The look and feel of the personalization is important, but that's only the beginning of what people can do with an open source design. Just as with app stores, some of these additions can be free, and some can come with a cost or a request for additional personal information to access the service, and all of this can be purchased through the digital wallet itself.

The key to a really good open source consortia project for the digital wallet is having focus towards maintaining the platform and then drawing on what works and pushing for constant improvement. With this kind of approach, digital wallets can develop to a high level of sophistication in a short period of time and create an experience that fulfills the variable needs of all users.

Chapter 6

Digital Identity

Digital identity is one of the cornerstones of the digital revolution. As the world moves towards digital identity solutions, we will need a place to store and use them. Digital identity is essential for having trustworthy, accountable digital and online systems, but many people are worried about digital identity. A common concern is that it will constitute a major loss of privacy as we move towards this tech-centric space.

While it's true that we will be putting more of our personal information on systems that are theoretically accessible to malicious actors, blockchain and associated technologies can actually make this information more secure and lead to more private operating environments for ourselves online.

Before discussing ways to securely store digital identities, however, it is important to understand what digital identities are and how they differ from other forms of identification and authentication.

Think about our driver's licence and all the information that's on it. Now imagine that instead of a plastic card we have a driver's licence that's printed on glass. If we take a hammer and shatter that glass into many tiny pieces, we have a lot of different little pieces of our identity. There's our name, separating our first name and our last name. Our date of birth, height, weight, eye colour, driver's licence number, etc. All these represent different components of our identity.

Under the paradigm of traditional identification, these little shards are useless. we have our name, but it's not attached to our date of birth. we couldn't get into a nightclub with an ID that had been cut up into little pieces.

Even if we have a whole card, the information preserved on it is static and limited. We have all sorts of information thrown together in an uncharted fashion. When we provide this identification to someone, we give them a lot of information that might not necessarily be needed in the specific context. The doorman at the nightclub needs to know our age, but does he really need to know our home address? This limits the security of our personal information and potentially limits when and to whom we want to present our documents.

Digital identity allows us to break down this information into separate little pieces, or "identity shards", while still allowing them to be useful for identification. A digital model allows us to choose what information we want to share in any given context without oversharing unnecessary information. We could present the nightclub bouncer with our verified photograph and a green check mark indicating that we are above the required age without showing him where we live, how much we weigh, our exact date of birth, or anything else we wouldn't ordinarily share with a stranger.

There are many applications for this. Think about when we sign up for a bank account and all the information that is required. They want to verify our identity and credit history and perhaps even our citizenship as well. We could go to a bank to open a new account only to learn they require all this information that we wouldn't want to carry around in our back pocket and subsequently don't have. If this information were stored within a digital wallet, though, we would always be able to securely access whatever it was that we needed.

The goal is to create a secure place to store all our different digital identities. Once we do, it will make signing up for services as easy as making a couple of clicks rather than engaging in a lengthy manual data entry process. No need to fill out many different forms, no need to scan photo IDs, no need to provide titles or proof of address. All these verified identities will be stored within a digital wallet, and the user will control what information to release to which agent.

A good example of this is loyalty cards. If we go to Canadian Tire or Shoppers Drug Mart or Walgreens, the cashier will often ask if we want to join their loyalty program. These programs collect consumer information and track their purchasing habits to help improve their product and services while at the same time offering exclusive benefits to loyalty members. If we say yes to the cashier, we will likely be given a card and an account number. We will likely be asked to fill out an online form for free points or some sort of promotion. This is where companies hope to get our valuable data and this is also where the collection methods can lead to bad data.

When we go to register our loyalty card we are often presented with a form that has many blank fields to it. A form where we manually enter our information. Sometimes the information required can be fairly personal, and we might not want to input it correctly. Or we might deliberately put in false information. we might want to collect the points but not want to give our real address because we worry about receiving junk mail or flyers. Even if this isn't the intention of the store, people can be irrational and sometimes deceptive regarding their private information.

Identity is an emotional subject for discussion. On the most fundamental level, there can be a discrepancy between what I want versus what I am. A person signing up for a credit card might inflate their annual income not because they are trying to commit fraud but because of their aspirational view of themselves. There can be a personal subjective aspect overlaid into that information.

The result of this for businesses is bad data. It's not accurate, and it doesn't help them improve their product selection or services. They're making decisions based on information that is not accurate, which is simply inefficient and ultimately leads to us paying more for goods and services.

What digital identity represents for the marketplace is an opportunity to have very concise and accurate data. In today's world, businesses are losing out because of the poor quality of the data they get from loyalty programs and the like.

Digital identity will streamline this process from a user perspective and greatly improve the quality of data collection from a business perspective. With a unified digital wallet, we could walk into a store, receive a message on our phone asking if we want to sign up for their loyalty program, and with the touch of a few buttons we could pass the necessary information to the store.

All future payments could be automatically associated with our loyalty program account, eliminating the need to produce another card from our wallet every time we make a purchase.

Today, many people who participate in these loyalty programs probably do not present their cards every time they make a purchase. we might be in a hurry or only buying a cold drink and paying in cash. This inconsistency also undermines the quality of the data.

There's also the issue of how companies store data collected through these programs. Storing client and customer data presents significant legal and reputation risks. We've seen the Home Depot hack. We've seen the Facebook/Cambridge Analytica hack. There was even an NSA hack where they lost millions of fingerprints and biometric data! Whenever we have large, centralized pools of data, it presents a target for hackers to go after. This vast amount of individual identity data can then be used for malicious purposes.

With digital identity, we don't actually need to provide the raw properties of identity. In many cases, we will be able to provide proof of particular things, such as residency, credit history, address, or membership for a service without them actually knowing our name or getting any personally identifiable information or PII. Once we have digital identity, we can do something called a zero-knowledge-proof.

A zero-knowledge-proof is a process of verifying a claim without actually viewing a document because we can trust the agent. For example, we can know that if the government issued my ID it has attested to the fact that I am Kyle Kemper. I am a Canadian citizen. That I was born on a particular date. The government can notarize all these shards of data in a form of digital identity. When I have this in my digital wallet, I can then provide other people and organizations with a "proof" to a question. Using the age example again, a business can make a

41

request from my wallet to determine if I am of legal drinking age. Because we have a government issued digital ID in our wallet it will be able to return "yes" without actually giving the exact date.

A notarized digital ID streamlines the verification process. When we go to rent a car, we don't have to produce a report showing that we passed our driving test. The physical driver's licence validates our claim to be a legal driver.

Digital identity will streamline this process even further and in many more applications. Once our digital identities are securely stored within our digital wallets, signing up for services will be faster, safer, and easier than ever before. The information stored in a self-sovereign and secure manner will empower us to hold these keys to our identities without relying on traditional plastic cards that expose sensitive information.

Digital identity can take many forms and creates many new opportunities for services. Digital identity can include work history, skills, certifications, reputation, and educational credentials — basically any kind of card or document or certification that we've ever received that attests to some sort of function or membership. It could include our phone number, email, Twitter username, Instagram, Facebook, LinkedIn accounts and more. Once all of them are connected in the wallet where we are the only person with authority over it, we will then be able to easily share information from any of these sources through any medium we choose. This will unlock additional kinds of services and offerings, which will in turn make products and services better.

Digital wallet users will be empowered to determine how much personal information they share and in what context. There may be a situation where someone requests information from us, but it would be up to us to determine what we want to share. Say that we walk into a store that's offering a promotion, and they want us to sign up to be notified about future promotions. We could receive a notification on our phone requesting that we provide contact information to be on a mailing list. We could accept or decline the request, determine what contact info if any we want to provide, and potentially provide feedback as to our reasoning.

Artificial intelligence will have a role in this as well. One application for artificial intelligence is assistants who help we with basic tasks based on our preferences. An artificial intelligence assistant will be able to help pick and choose what information we want to share with the services we are interacting with. These assistants will learn from our choices and could, for example, automatically flag notifications from a service we have repeatedly declined or further restrict access to personal information we are particularly sensitive about.

The key thing that an open digital wallet will represent is an opportunity to have a consistent, interoperable place to hold our digital keys. It will safeguard our digital identity data and make it easy to hold, store, send, request, and prove the different components of digital identity.

When we have control we can decide what data we want to share. Certain apps might request access to data, but it will be easier to limit the data that is shared to what is absolutely necessary and to reduce the superfluous data that is held by the companies we interact with.

We're seeing a need for access to digital identity to be entirely determined by the user. People don't want companies to have access to all their personal information anymore because they recognize that these large pools of data are targets for malicious actors. Data sovereignty means being able to cut off any request for data we don't want to provide and decentralizing how this data is stored. It's about putting us in control and not hiding our loss of control in unreadable service-level agreements. That is something we need to move past in order to move forward.

Digital identity is one of the cornerstones of the open digital wallet. It represents personal identity as part of a personal identity management system. It can both encapsulate one's personal information and also one's corporate information, health records, or any other type of data we have about ourselves.

Once we have standardized places to store this data, we will be poised for the next wave of adoption of blockchain and identity services. There will be a proliferation of true real-world applications at the consumer, enterprise, and government levels. Digital identity will empower consumers, improve the quality of data collection, and in turn revolutionize the delivery of products and services.

Chapter 7

Payment Experience

Payment is an enormous industry all in itself. If we look at some of the leading payment processors in the world, we have Visa, Mastercard, and American Express on the credit side. In Canada, we have such things as Interac. Globally, we have the C Plus Network. We have PayPal and Venmo, the SWIFT Banking Network, and many new payment services are appearing in Europe and Asia that we don't have access to in the North American market.

The payment industry has considerable physical infrastructure. We need a physical card to use many of these services, connecting to ATMs and point-of-sale machines. Many receipts have to be printed to facilitate these exchanges. That's paper and ink being used and oil-based plastic to build all these machines.

Then we also have cash. The government takes responsibility for printing bank notes and minting coins. These notes inevitably become bacteria colonies presenting a health risk to all who interact with them. Moving, counting, and securing physical banknotes requires significant resource investments. It takes a lot of money and resources so that we can use physical money. It costs even more to assure there are systems in place to make payments that are reliable, private, and relatively secure.

We're starting to see the beginnings of change. We're starting to see iPads used to process transactions in stores and restaurants, producing a digital receipt instead of a printed one. It's still in the early stages, but this is where everything is headed.

Within the legacy payment system are ISO standards that payment companies abide by. Digital currencies paired with a unified wallet platform stand to reform and revolutionize the payments space. What is key to understand about the current system is that it only appears to be easy and secure. In fact, in the background are countless actors extracting value, adding friction, and imposing delays that ultimately result in us paying higher prices for goods and services. There are great opportunities to make payments seamless and safe using digital identity, digital currencies, and a unified digital wallet.

Think about how cash works. Right now there is no record of a transaction when we pay in cash. There are just these paper/plastic/cloth bills going from one person to another. If we get a paper receipt, it isn't tied to the cash we paid with in any way, and there's always a risk that the bills are fraudulent or counterfeit. The issuer takes steps to make it difficult to duplicate, but merchants must always risk that they are being paid with fake money.

With credit cards, there's a risk of chargeback. If someone uses a stolen credit card, the merchant will provide services, but when the owner of the card reports it stolen, the credit card company can then go back and remove the money from the merchant's account. This is called a chargeback.

I may go to Walmart and buy a whole host of goods with my Visa card. At the end of the month, I get my statement. It shows me how much I spent at Walmart on that day, but that's it. The paper receipt I received when I made the purchase has a detailed account of what I bought, but it's still somewhat limited. If I look at my statement and ask myself what I bought at Walmart, I have only this paper receipt to consult. I may not have saved it, or it may not be easy to identify particular items. The information is limited and spread out over many different systems.

The opportunity that we have with digital payments and wallets is to be able to store asset or product tokens as well. That big purchase from Walmart, for example, could send a detailed receipt to my wallet comprising the names and product information of everything purchased, including any titles or warranties that may have been associated with that purchase. I would be identified as the owner of those goods by holding these tokens in my digital wallet.

This is related to a concept in supply chain management known as provenance tracking, which means tracking the origins of an item through all the steps in the supply chain or its history of ownership.

When referring to payments, we have the opportunity at checkout to be able to have all these digital tokens passed to us and a digital receipt passed to our wallet that has all the details about the payment experience we have just concluded.

When both parties to an exchange have digital wallets, we can have an exceptional payment experience. The buyer presents his goods to the merchant, who requests an amount in payment, and then the buyer it notified, reviews and makes the payment. This can be done using digital currencies, such as Bitcoin, Ethereum, Dash, and Litecoin. Or it can be done in digital dollars or bank transfers as well. Fees may be involved for accepting less-popular currencies, but the future will be an era of choice.

There is also an opportunity to attach survey or feedback mechanisms to any kind of payment experience. Individuals can be incentivized to provide feedback in the form of discounts or rewards, and this will improve service delivery and lead to better quality analysis. There's also the ability to incentivize other kinds of engagement, such as social engagement. A brand could provide us with rewards when we become a fan of their service on Facebook or perhaps tweet about it, and all this could be triggered through our digital wallet in a couple clicks.

This feedback experience can be made much simpler, which will encourage more people to engage in a payment system that improves the quality of data collection. Rather than filling out an onerous form, it will be more like the Uber feedback model, where we give a star rating to questions. These questions can be provided directly from within the app and consumers will be incentivized to provide additional information with every payment. The result is that we end up providing significant amount of quality data and are rewarded for our input. These rewards can be structured in a way that consumers who take more time to provide feedback will receive greater reward.

One of the keys for adoption to digital currencies in general is how do we create a payment experience that is an order of magnitude better than the current one. I'm a firm believer that the proliferation of digital receipts will create a feedback loop where people want to keep their documentation in one place. Be it digital receipts, digital warranties, or digital titles, it's too complicated to store all this information when it is printed on paper. We need to make it easy to collect these documents and transfer them to others if we sell or give these products to other people. This will provide an overall experience boost that will put legacy payment methods in the rear-view mirror.

The current payment experience has considerable room for improvement. Chargebacks represent a threat to merchants, payment delays create challenges to the processing of orders, and online shopping shows that consumers are eager to adopt new experiences that are easier, faster, and more secure.

For online shopping, digital wallets can significantly streamline the payment process. We could be able to queue up our cart as normal and then pay by scanning a code or inputting a PIN presented to our phone. A connection between ourselves and the merchant will be established that we can validate from our secure wallet. We will need our digital wallet on us to execute a payment, making it more secure than entering our credit card information into a form. If we're making a purchase from an online source we've never used before, this will also save us from entering our address and billing information into their system, which we may not be able to trust.

The digital wallet will become the primary means of demonstrating ownership of something. We will hold the keys that declare our ownership of all items held within our digital wallet, and then those, the actual items they represent, can be stored on an industry blockchain. There can be a Samsung blockchain, an Apple blockchain, and a blockchain that isn't controlled by a specific manufacturer but by an entire industry. This will push back against the centralized database approach, putting ownership in the hands of the owners themselves, and resulting in more efficient and effective systems.

Kyle Kemper

In terms of payment experience, the era of choice will facilitate the interoperability of digital currencies. People will be able to choose what kind of value they want to store, and merchants will be able to choose what type of money they'd like to receive. The wallet and payment solution will provide the ability for consumers to pay with whatever currency they want to and for merchants to receive whatever currency they prefer. There will be a calculation of an exchange rate and perhaps a processing fee based on the variables.

But the consequence of this is that individual consumers will be able to make payments anywhere to anyone as easily as they would at their corner store. Consider the payment experience of the international traveler. When we're in another country, we have to go and get local fiat cash and hope that the banking system will work and connect to our home account. We may be forced to use something such as a Visa payment solution and be exposed to generally high exchange rates. When we go to buy something, we have to calculate how much it costs in our home country's currency.

The global payment experience using digital wallets will be much simpler. We'll be able to purchase goods anywhere in the world using the currencies we have, and merchants will be able to accept the currency as is or instantly convert it to their preferred currency.

This technology will revolutionize the payment experience. It will offer a significantly improved experience based on choice, feedback loops, loyalty integration, speed, and security. Yes please.

Chapter 8

Healthcare, Succession, Legal, and Voting Applications

There are many problems that a unified digital wallet can solve. The digital wallet is a platform that brings together commerce, identification, and records management, paving the way for innovation. An open source design approach combined with robust APIs and new standards will allow people to take this technology and run with it, creating a new generation of digital applications that leverage blockchain, AI, deep learning, automation, and other technologies.

There are some specific applications where the potential of this technology is highly apparent — where there is a great need for more secure means of holding and sharing privileged information. In this chapter, we'll cover some healthcare, succession planning, legal, and voting uses.

In the current medical system, we have a problem with how medical records are held and distributed. As it is now, doctors and hospitals maintain their own servers, where they securely store all our electronic health and medical records, but that's only if these records have been digitized. More often than not, they use filing cabinets filled with paper records.

The issue is that they're the ones in possession of our data. We are able to ask them for it, and they have to provide it to us, but that process can be cumbersome, lengthy, and our complete medical history may be stored across several different servers and filing cabinets belonging to different institutions and specialists.

Some doctors like this status quo, as it gives them power and control over our data, but many practitioners also realize that it's kind of ridiculous and adds unnecessary complexities and liability. If we visit a new doctor, they have to call our old one to transfer our medical records. Since these are our medical records, if we want to share them, we should be able to. If we find ourselves in another part of the world and need to see an expert, we want to be able to give that person immediate access to our records.

Digital wallets and digital keys offer a solution. This technology allows for the immediate provisioning of this information in a secure way at our discretion. This will save lives by creating faster access to critical health information.

The data in our medical records comprises many different kinds of information. Some records are notes made by our doctor. Some records are results of tests. There is also basic health information like our blood type, height, weight, allergies, etc.

Kyle Kemper

During an emergency, we want to have access to as much of this information as possible. We can predict what information will be necessary while also being cognizant that there is rarely time to collect pertinent information from different sources.

With a digital wallet, storing this information will be as easy as storing an emergency contact. It will be possible to broadcast this emergency data so that doctors can automatically access our information should it be required. If it's not an emergency and more detailed sensitive information is requested, we can provide it to medical professionals through multisignature key technology aka "multisig." With this method, we can require different people to sign a transaction in order to share or access information. Using multisig, signatories, such as a family member, caretaker, or recognized healthcare provider, could be authorized to access health information from our digital wallet even if we are incapacitated.

With a unified wallet, we will be the ones who control access to the primary versions of our medical records. Our records are our records, and we want to be able to share them when necessary.

Our health records and the access logs for the information also gets stronger with blockchain technology because they become immutable. This means that when a doctor makes a note on our file the record of that addition get logged permanently. If a doctor makes a mistake in something they commit to our file, they can correct it through an amendment or a new note but not by deleting evidence of the mistake. This is important in the case of misdiagnosis or if a doctor's action leads to an adverse effect. Accountability is important, and that can be achieved by preserving the record.

When we think about the changing role of healthcare, it's important to consider how a more patient-centric ownership model of data will be at the forefront of this development. Digital wallets allow us to be the one with primary control over our data. It allows us to set emergency contacts who can access that data if we're incapacitated or what key medical information will be released to healthcare professionals and institutions. We can even be incentivized to share data in exchange for compensation. When it comes to health research, data is expensive and the better the quality the more valuable. Our health data could help us earn value while also helping keep us healthy.

If we think about emergency contacts, one of the problems with our current system is that we in danger if our single contact is unavailable. The beauty of digitization, wallets, and push notifications is that we have the ability to create a prioritized list that puts forth a second emergency contact if the first is not available, and so on. This list can run through family members, peers, and colleagues so that someone we trust is empowered to release certain information to a doctor, hospital, or paramedic as required.

Kyle Kemper

Then there's the matter of standardization of data. Consider the example of a prescription for eyeglasses. When this data is standardized across optometrists, glasses manufacturers, and contact manufacturers, it becomes possible to radically streamline the product delivery process. We could break our glasses and immediately buy replacements through our digital wallet that contains our prescription, the model of frames we last bought, our face dimensions, and anything else. Within a few minutes, an identical replacement set could be shipped straight to our door.

Working with global optometry associations, it should be possible to establish a clear set of standards that could operate within the framework of a digital wallet to make this process seamless. There would be a standard digital prescription that I can instantly share with my optometrist to provide them with the information needed to fill my order. This standardization exists today it just needs to be imported into a wallet schema.

This technology will also interact favourably with wearable devices. Futurists predict that the cell phone will not be particularly important in the future, with its functions replaced by wearables and bio-integrations that will open up many new applications.

Smart glasses, watches, or implants will allow for brain monitoring and other forms of sensors. Once there is interoperability among these things, it will be possible for something like a Fitbit to authenticate our wallet and add data from our workout to our medical records.

Wearables are also important for sharing vital health information. For a long time, people with deadly allergies have had to wear bracelets that act as universal indicators of their condition. In the same fashion, a digital wallet could be set up to have a persistent broadcast about some critical information concerning our health.

This technology can also open up a whole wonderful world of utilizing our health data for greater causes. Data collection and research is a massive industry within the healthcare industry. Health companies pay lots of money to patients and third parties for research. Quality data, cross-referencing, and deep analysis is something that can be unlocked via our digital wallet once we control our records.

Digital wallets will allow this process to be done much more quickly and efficiently. Researchers and scientists will be able to contact patients with a common disease, condition or characteristic and request them to share their medical data to their research pool. They will be able to incentivize this sharing through payments made directly to the patient's wallet. The result will be access to incredibly organized data that will drive medical breakthroughs.

Artificial intelligence will have a role in this as well. Digital wallets compile a great amount of verifiable information about ourselves, our habits, and our health. By lowering the cost of collecting this information, we improve the quality of research. There are legitimate privacy concerns about sharing this kind of information too freely, which has been holding back researchers but with Blockchain and digital wallets we have a breakthrough.

Digital wallets paired with artificial intelligence and deep learning environments will allow us to share pertinent information with researchers while protecting the privacy of individual patients. It's the same approach to managing digital identities to share relevant verified information without sharing irrelevant personally identifiable information.

An AI will be able to access an incredible amount of secured information to allow for deep learning. Because this information is de-identified, it doesn't really matter if it is a researcher or an AI who has access to it. But there is the potential for an AI or a deep learning environment to have access to information that researchers typically wouldn't.

This is all highly speculative at this point, and this application is not a primary area of my expertise. I can say with certainty that there is great potential to use this technology to revolutionize medical research, records management, and treatment options.

Legal Applications

There is a wide range of legal applications for this technology. Think about death. Think about succession. What happens when we die? Right now, there's a major concern about control and access to keys regarding cryptocurrency. If we hold crypto, we might have a private key that nobody can ever access unless we tell them what it is. If we die and we've not shared it, those digital assets are basically rendered unusable.

That's value that our heirs and children will not have access to, but with a digital wallet, there's the ability to create succession plans. There is even an opportunity to create what's called a dead man's switch in case we haven't properly planned.

A dead man's switch in a digital wallet is an application concept whereby our wallet can pass our assets to others after a prolonged period of inactivity. If we haven't logged in to our wallet for a year or however long we choose to set it, it will go into succession mode and start transferring access of keys to designated identities that we have chosen.

Having a succession plan is very important for digital assets and identities. We need to have a mechanism in place if we want our heirs to control our digital assets, just as we want to have a plan in place for our family to access our social profiles upon passing. Keys need to be secure so that we can control them but also be transferable in the event of our inevitable transition.

Think about the current succession process. We can sit down with a lawyer and go through all our assets, deciding who's going to get what and how it will all be broken down. With a digital wallet, there is the potential to create apps that handle succession planning. We will be able to go through the assets and the tokens of ownership in the wallet and decide whom to transfer them to directly.

The title for my car will go to my daughter, and the boat will go to my son. My wealth in the form of my digital assets is to be divided across the whole family, and any information that we want preserved and passed on can be delegated in the same way.

The digital wallet will also hold some information that we don't need or want to pass on to other people. My bank info, crypto, and titles, yes, but I don't really need anybody to take over my fantasy hockey account. If we have adult entertainment accounts, we probably don't want our children getting that information. A digital wallet with an integrated succession plan can ensure that certain information ends with us.

The sensitive, private things that we don't want to share with anyone or that don't really matter do not need to be passed along, but we should be able to identify which keys should be included and which should not so that there is a seamless transference when one passes on.

These succession plans need not distribute assets to individuals either. We could determine, for example, that some portion of our digital assets be given to charities, institutions, individuals, or communities.

Making succession planning digital and programmable creates a hotbed for innovation within this space. We can't predict what people will come up with, but the more accessible the unified digital wallet system is, the better solutions the ecosystem can create for securing our legacy.

The applications for this kind of technology will have profound implications for other aspects of the legal profession. "Smart contracts" stand to streamline many processes. Basic contract law can be streamlined in a way that let people engage in digital handshakes that self-execute based on inputs.

One concept that is changing the nature of the organization is the concept called a Decentralized Autonomous Organizations, or a DAO. A DAO is a foundation-less or corporation-less, leaderless organization that self-executes according to the system's conditions.

This is a new model that is being explored and examined, but the idea is that we can participate in a DAO through the keys held in our wallet, granting us voting abilities to direct the actions within these organizations, systems, teams, projects, or whatever they may be, based on our stake in the DAO.

This will have a significant effect on the legal profession. The entire way that law and contracts work will shift, leading to a change in the basic function and activities of lawyers. Many of these basic functions can be incorporated into smart contracts, where using legal apps or services will allow us to negotiate an agreement with another party and sign off on it.

We traditionally use lawyers to put money into escrow. Now, we can just use digital currencies and digital escrow services to hold money on the side until payment or services have been delivered. Taking deposits and executing wills is one thing, but regarding corporate structuring, options, stocks, and bonds, all these forms of compensation can be codified directly into smart contracts that execute based on completion, or not executed based on non-completion the of outlined tasks.

This kind of trust protocol backed by blockchain allows the various ecosystem parties to witness the interactions within and confirm that the contract has been fulfilled and the services accomplished or not. For example, only when a result has been verified is payment released.

This can be applied to the media industry. Say we're in preproduction and when that is complete, we go to production. A day of filming takes place, those responsible verify that certain actions were accomplished and as a result everyone who worked gets paid instantly for their efforts. Everyone's contributions are recorded in the project master file, and the process repeats through the rest of the project.

We can move away from structures that rely on infrequent major milestones and move into a much more liquid approach to execution of micro-milestones. The development and execution of projects can be tailored to much more short-term scheduling, reflecting the realities of the creation of content or film. For example, when we're creating content or a film, we have lots of different people working on it through different pay structures. Some people are just getting paid for their effort and then move on to other fixed-rate work, but others may have more interest in the project, taking a lower rate of pay in exchange for royalties or equity.

With smart contracts and blockchain, when a piece of content starts earning revenue, it can instantly be split according to the terms negotiated. In this system, there'll be no difference between the freelancing editor and the executive producer working for royalties. Each has their own conditions, but it will settle instantly.

Currently, very large discrepancies exist in settlement times between different people in the media industry. Using smart contracts, it will split and settle instantly.

Once we have secure verified information that is easily shareable, massive changes will occur in fields such as medicine and law that are currently dominated by small classes of professionals. People will control their own data, manage their own contracts, and be able to verify and interact with their ecosystems with unparalleled ease.

Blockchain Voting

There are many "holy grails" of blockchain technology, and one of which is voting and elections. Securely voting from our digital wallet is coming. The implications are enormous. I believe it will lead to more participation, higher voter turnout, more informed voting decisions, and a more active democracy.

In the near future, we will be able to receive a voting token to our digital wallet and be able to cast it from wherever we are. We will no longer need to go to a polling station. We will also be able to get in-depth information about the candidates we are voting for and their stance on the relevant issues. In my voting experience, when I get a ballot, there are people and parties I don't even know about. With digital voting, it's possible for there to be links and additional information about the candidates. This will reduce the efficiency of heavy advertising campaigns based purely on name/colour/party recognition and lead to more informed voting decisions.

A common concern is the privacy of one's vote. This can be addressed through the use of vote tumblers and mixers that disassociate the digital ballot from the voter. One of the great benefits of the blockchain technology is that we will be able to verify that our vote was cast and recorded properly, without disclosing our identity. This will allow for unprecedented transparency and trust in the voting system itself.

Vote digitization presents an opportunity for delegative democracy, a concept where we are able to assign our votes to people whose judgment we trust on a given subject. For example, I really trust my friend Andreas regarding cybersecurity. I could assign my votes to him relating to these subjects. My friend Ron is a constitutional expert whom I respect and trust, so for anything relating to this he can direct my vote.

Referendums can also become more frequent and effective. Once people have a digital voice through a digital vote, it is possible for outdated laws to be challenged and overturned by the people. It's important to remember that in a representative democratic system the government serves the people, and the people don't serve the government. Blockchain technology, digital voting, and a unified digital wallet can usher in a new age of societal governance. Governance by the people, of the people, and for the people.

Chapter 9

Security

Security is a major issue concerning digital wallets. An open digital wallet is going to host our identity, digital assets, certifications, wills, contracts, health data, votes and so many other types of information.

This information is sensitive and valuable to us. It is our personal black box. It's critically important that we're the only ones who have access to it, and that we have methods in place to ensure that if we lose access to a device we will not lose all our information.

The same broad security concerns about the wallet in our pocket apply to a digital wallet. We don't want to lose it. We don't want it to fall into the wrong person's hands. The advantage of a digital wallet over a physical wallet is that we don't lose the keys that protect our security if our phone falls into the wrong person's hands. If someone gets our physical wallet, they can abuse our credit cards, identifications, and cash with practical impunity. With a digital wallet, it is locked and we are the key.

With Bitcoin, our private keys are basically the passwords that allow us to move our money, but when other types of information are involved,

Kyle Kemper

especially digital identities, we need to be as certain as possible that they are accessible and secure.

It's bad if our money is lost or stolen, but it can be much worse if our identity is stolen. I know from first-hand experience.

Recently someone created a fake ID and pretended they were me at a retail branch of Rogers telecom in Canada. They asked the person at the outlet to reassign my mobile number to a device that they were in control of. They were successful and for almost 11 hours they were able to make calls, receive calls, send text messages and receive text messages using my number. The attack that they most often perform is they go to our gmail accounts and try and reset the password with a text message. Many people use SMS password recovery with gmail and if someone has our phone number they can reset out gmail password and BAM! they have access to our digital selves. They will change the main password, and then start digging to find ways they can either steal from us directly or extort us into paying a ransom. It is downright evil and can ruin lives. All of this because someone can simply present a fake piece of ID to a front-line corporate soldier; soldiers who can also be corrupted. This problem goes away with a secure key/certificate that we can store in our digital wallet.

The open digital wallet will allow us to store certificates and keys for all sorts of different services so we can securely authenticate our identities and interact with them.

We can ensure that only us have access to our digital wallet using a variety of authentication methods. We can use passwords, PINs, fingerprints, biometrics, facial scans, and other more sophisticated measures.

There are ways of authenticating ourselves that make use of what are called unique dynamic identifiers. A fingerprint is a biometric identifier but it is static. We're the only one who has our fingerprint, and it doesn't change, but because it doesn't change, someone could theoretically copy our fingerprint and use the copy to falsely authenticate a service. We can make it additionally secure if we combine it with a PIN or password.

But PINs and passwords are problematic because we can forget them or they can be captured by key-loggers and viruses. We are already inundated with services requiring unique PINs and passwords, and most people reuse or use similar ones just to be able to remember them all.

A major part of the problem with security is the centralization of data. When all information is stored in one place, it is a more valuable target for hacking. Hackers will devote significant resources to crack even the most impressive security system because the reward is access to many people's data...a honey pot of data.

Decentralizing data will upend these incentives. If they have to put a lot of work into hacking a system and the result is only a single person's data, it will hardly be worth their time to hack people's accounts.

This is the lesson to be learned from the cases of Home Depot, Equifax, Facebook, Cambridge Analytica, and countless others. When we distribute and become the owners of our data, we will be in charge of our keys, and that will change the very nature of the security discussion.

There are many different approaches to security. There's local storage, which means the information is stored on the device itself, but this can be problematic if we lose our device. There are wallets that provide a backup seed phrase that acts as our master key just in case we lose our device. In this case, we need to write a sequence of words down in a secure place and ensure that it doesn't fall into the wrong hands. With a master seed phrase, we can install a wallet on a new device and enter the master phrase which will then recover the private keys stored in that wallet.

This is effective when we're holding digital currencies, but it becomes more difficult when we're hosting all sorts of different information, including digital identities, transaction logs, passwords, credentials, contacts, stocks, bonds, titles, etc. The main threat is if your backup seed phrase falls into the wrong hands you can be compromised completely.

So how do we pick the best solution? The approach that I believe in is to encourage competition so that the best solutions emerge. There are many security and authentication services and approaches on the market. An open and competitive wallet platform involves not relying on a single security service or technology for the wallet but rather allowing people to choose from a wide variety of different services. If we feel confident in SMS verification, we can use that. If we want fingerprints or some other biometric, we can use that. The open approach will also allow for the community to validate, score, and recommend the best solutions to ensure that we are the only ones able to access our wallet.

It will be possible to buy wristbands, rings, and other wearables that can act as authenticators based on our heartbeat. Headbands or smart glasses could be outfitted with a miniature ECG built in that measures our brain waves are possible.

Brainwaves and heartbeats are known as Unique Dynamic Identifiers (UDI), meaning they are not constant. They do not stay the same, but they are unique to each person, so we can always verify our identity based on them.

UDIs represent a major improvement over a Static Unique Identifier, which is something like a fingerprint. our fingerprint doesn't change, making it copyable, but the way our brain operates, the way we walk or talk or breathe, the way our heart beats, those things cannot be replicated so easily but can be used to authenticate us.

Pulling back for a moment, let's consider what we are storing in our digital wallets. We have all these different kinds of keys corresponding to different currencies, identifiers, and documentation. It's like having all these different keys on a single keychain. How do we make sure that we can have it on devices that could be lost or stolen and still be secure?

One possibility that is being explored is using decentralized storage solutions. Services such as IPFS, Storj, or Filecoin aim to allow us to store a secure encrypted file in a distributed fashion in the global storage cloud.

When we log in to our wallet, we could be able to pull down this encrypted file and then it will be up to the authentication mechanism we have chosen for our wallet to unlock it and provide access to the keys. This will ensure that if we lose all our devices or if we're stranded, we'll still be able to recover all the information that's contained in our digital wallet.

How do we guarantee the security of these systems? How can we have a succession plan in place that will manage our assets after we die and be sure that it will be immune to hacking?

Right now, people can secure their wallets, phones, computers, homes, and other things in many different ways. We can have a lock and key for the front door of our house, or we can have a whole security system. We have an open source model for physical security.

A similar approach should be taken for the digital wallet. We need to encourage competition between authentication services to ensure that the companies that provide these services are always working to improve the security of their products. Open APIs for authentication will allow the best in the business to compete to make the most secure, resilient, and robust solutions imaginable — one that will be able to service future generations as we move into the age of digital identity, digital currencies, digital assets, digital receipts, and seamless experience.

Chapter 10

Inclusivity by Design

Inclusivity is key to ensuring that the benefits of digital currencies and blockchain reach every corner of the world. A unified digital wallet can give people worldwide access to digital identity and financial services as never before.

Digital wallets are something that the entire world will need access to. Bitcoin has provided the world access to the first global, decentralized financial system. All one needs to access it is a computer, a phone, or some other method to hold the keys. It can be technical but it can also have physical and rudimentary dimensions as well, but what's important is that everybody is able to access and participate in this system.

Setting up a bitcoin wallet is akin to opening a bank account. Actually, it's more like becoming your own bank. For billions of people on the planet banking is something they have not had access to. With bitcoin they can skip banks just like many skipped landlines.

The same must be true with identity. Estimates suggest that over 1B people don't have valid ID. 1,000,000,000+ people! Enter digital identity and the digital wallet. This is an enabling technology that will allow those who have been excluded to leapfrog the legacy financial and identity systems and unlock countless new opportunities while disrupting the collective reliance on the cards, the banks, the plastic and paper, and the centralized record keepers. We sit on the precipice of a digital golden age, an age where we have leveraged the fact that we live in a globally connected environment, where we have wireless connectivity, distributed computing, distributed storage, artificial intelligence, 3D printing, autonomous vehicles, unlimited energy and sharing economies.

The entire world should be able to store their information securely under individual control and be able to share their information as they choose without these interactions becoming burdensome.

The digital wallet will provide an accessible and inclusive space for all. If we think about the development side, this is reflected in an open source ethos where anybody on the planet can develop apps and solutions that add to the wallet.

This is the difference between the Apple and Android approaches to their platforms. Apple is the walled garden where we need approval. Android permits anybody to build apps and install them directly. We need to approach this like Android.

Inclusivity must inform design principles. When we have open standards and APIs, we basically create extensions or apps for the wallet, and they become listed for everyone to access. It creates the ability for this thing to become dynamic and grow and for innovators to develop new solutions that fill gaps and solve problems.

Inclusivity also means crossing borders as well. In China, there's something termed the Great Firewall that allows only certain kinds of applications to run there and permits users to access only certain sources of information.

In Canada, the U.S., and Europe, it's more open. In other countries, not so much. By using cryptocurrency, digital wallets, and decentralized protocols, there's the potential to really open up development and embrace a new paradigm for the interaction of individuals, companies, groups, teams, governments, and intelligence. It's about giving people the freedom to build on top of this.

There is always the need to make sure the systems are safe, secure, and resilient. Feedback systems, self-regulatory organizations, and consumer protection initiatives can help ensure that the technology is being steered in the right direction — one that is effective, efficient, and socially conscious.

Principles of privacy by design and self-sovereignty are essential. They are what will empower us as individuals to control our data. Open digital wallets can facilitate a transfer of power from the age of corporate dominance to self-sovereignty. The digital wallet can prompt the development of codes of ethics, standards, and privacy that include reporting mechanisms for when apps or solutions are threatening the security of an individual's data and assets.

Inclusivity can be at the foundation of an organization or consortium that will work towards developing an open digital wallet. We're going to need to have stakeholders from all around the world involved in the development and creation of this concept. It can't just be a pay-to-play environment that is relegated to a few major integrators. If we want to unify people all over the world, we need to ensure that representatives from all over are involved.

This involves governments, corporations, individuals, privacy experts, designers, security experts, cryptographers, academics, philosophers, activists, law enforcement, NGOs and more — basically all the different people who recognize the benefit of this idea and who will work towards realizing this enabling technology which I've described as the unified digital wallet.

Once we have this base enabler, this unified digital wallet, it will open up a wonderful world of opportunity. Through a framework that encourages open source design, inclusivity, collaboration, and creation we can be successful. A framework that creates competition among service providers can lead to better apps and better services.

Kyle Kemper

We will see the rise of new apps and solutions that we can't even imagine. WHERE THERE'S A WILL, THERE'S A WAY.

Chapter 11

A Golden Age is Upon Us

Civilization is going through a transition. We are moving from the Age of Pisces into the Age of Aquarius. This is part of the 26k year cycle known as the procession of the equinoxes. During an age change, there is a transition of consciousness. Over the course of the last century, we have seen technological innovation that has affected billions of people. The planet's population continues to grow, but we are showing that we are capable of managing this growth. We are moving into an age of abundance. We have enough food to feed everyone. We have enough shelter to house everyone. We have enough clothing to clothe everyone. Unfortunately, the value structure of civilization has not made these priorities. Greed, power, and status have led the few to dominate the many.

The status quo is changing with blockchain technology, cryptocurrencies, the sharing economy, artificial intelligence, genetics, 3D-printing, energy innovation, cleantech, and other exponential technologies. People are converging to create. Take burning man for example, where 10 principles (Radical-Inclusion, Radical-Self-Expression, Radical-Self-Reliance, Gifting, Decommodification, Civic Responsibility, Leave No Trace, Communal Effort, Participation & Immediacy) inspire the community to create one of the greatest gatherings on the planet.

In recent years I have been exploring this convergence, and it is clear to me that a unified wallet is a keystone to this shift. Its creation and maintenance will give the people of the world a portal to securely and effectively participate in this new paradigm. I believe that the time is near when we will see convergence towards the concepts outlined in this book and a global activation take place to create the unified digital wallet. All the pieces of the puzzle are on the table. The task ahead of us now is putting them together.

This book is far from perfect. I do not have all the answers. I do not seek control over the direction. I aim to inspire others and plant the seeds of what is possible. For some, this may trigger action and a desire to participate and collaborate. For other, it may trigger a desire for more education, and for others, it may do nothing. Whatever the effect, it simply is. I am not entirely certain what the exact next steps are, but forces have led me to create and release my thoughts in the form of this book and I hope they have resonated with you in some form or fashion.

"Be Truthful, Fearless, and Gentle" is a quote that resonates with me and guides me. Perhaps it can help guide you too.

W LOVE & GRATITUDE

KYLE KEMPER

Acknowledgments & Gratitude

This book is made possible thanks to the love and support of a great many people. For the past five years, I've dedicated my heart and spirit to crypto and blockchain technology. It has been a journey that has taken me around the world and allowed me to directly connect with thousands of incredible people.

First, my deepest gratitude to Michael Thompson, my friend, producer, and the creator of Peacock Books, who has guided me through the book process. His willingness to teach, guide, prod me, and work with me through this experience is the reason this book exists. If you are considering writing a book, I highly suggest Michael – PeacockBooks.co

To my coauthor, Arlen Mighton, for his time, dedication, and understanding of my visions.

To my launch manager Cody Smith for your guidance, wisdom, and encouragement.

To my cosmic love Brittany Lindstrom, you are a fountain of love, joy, creativity and energy in my life. I love you with my heart, soul, and spirit. There is no limit to what is possible together. To your radiant son Bowen and to the seeds we planted in the Giant Forest of Sequoia National Park.

To my mother, Margaret, who for years has been pushing me to write a book. I have witnessed firsthand how through her writings and lectures she has been helping individuals all over the world understand and appreciate their mental health. I love you mum and you inspire me to be the best I can be.

To my father, Fried, who has taught me so much, supported me, and been there for me as my entrepreneurial and artistic endeavours have led me to where I am today.

To Sasha Cunningham for her love and support and for being an incredible mother to our two amazing children. To her father, Patrick, his wife, Karin, her mother, Leesha, and her brothers, Rowan and William.

To my children, Amelia Snow and John Wolf; I love you with all my heart and soul, and the work that I do is so that the world we grow up in is as magical as possible.

To my brother Justin, who has taught me through his actions and words the value in listening, connecting, and inspiring people. To Sophie for her energy, creativity, and spirituality. To my nephews and niece Xavier, Ella, and Hadrien.

To my brother Sacha, who has been a deep inspiration and teacher to me. To Zoe for her love, support, and generosity. To my nephew and nieces Pierre, Gala, and Ariane.

Kyle Kemper

To my sister Alicia, who has always been a source of love, inspiration, and confidence.

To my brother Michel, a child of the earth who was taken by the mother; you help guide me spiritually as I walk my path.

To all the Kempers, Tremblays, Sinclairs, Walkers, and Dennings; I wish I could name every one of we here.

To my Ottawa boys, les boys . . . Hugh Denton, Brian Hermon, Zach Kathnelson, Nick Laidlaw, Max Lizondo, Ted Mirsky, Nick Paget, Justin Parker, Lee Piazza, Mike Prior, Mike Armbruster . . . oh yeah, and also to les girls . . .

To my great friend, father, and fellow entrepreneur Charley Lazaro.

To Horia Lambrache, one of the first digital wizards in my life whose entrepreneurial spirit and dedication have been a massive inspiration.

To the Anderson Family: Nick, Oli, Alex, Charlotte, and George; you are like a second family for me.

To the thousands of people from all over the world who have inspired me, taught me, worked with me, and influenced me and this book.

To Adrian Turchet for helping activate this book and for pursuing a film that helps visualize the concepts.

To fellow ashaman, crypto veteran, and u.Cash founder Ageesen Sri for all the support, advice, and presence over the years.

To the brilliant and energetic Joseph Weinberg for telling it like it is, thinking big, and for being an incredible global ambassador.

To Sunny Ray for being an amazing community activator and visionary. To Phil Leibowski four the agreements and much more.

To Emma Todd for her friendship, support, and help over the years.

To Andreas Antonopolous for being an ambassador, educator, and hero to the community. Your speech at the 2014 Bitcoin Expo in Toronto first lit me up to what's possible.

To Tim Bouma, a great ambassador and educator relating to all things digital identity and verified claims. Deepest gratitude for your wonderful foreword. To our most excellent mutual friend and wallet expert Darrell O'Donnell. Together we are all working to ensure the world has secure, private, self-sovereign identity.

Kyle Kemper

To the prolific author, speaker, and visionary Don Tapscott, who has been educating millions of people about the potential of Blockchain through his writings and speeches. To Salim Ishmail for showcasing millions the potential of exponentiality and how we need to think critically about out next steps.

To the great connector, world-bridger, and cross-pollinator Nathon Gunn.

To my Social Wallet family, including James Wilson, Jack Cable, Alex Hudson, Marshall Swatt, Brooks Hunter, Joseph Onorati, Reed Holmes, Alex Voto, and many more. Social Wallet was a very ambitious project that failed on the first go, but through failure comes experience. Deep gratitude for all our support, effort and love.

To the peace-seeking planetary warrior Mike Zuckerman.

To Marcellus Mindle for our design thinking sessions, deep discussions, and expert facilitation.

To Steffen Christensen, Marcus Ballinger and the team at Policy Horizons Canada, the futurist arm of the Canadian Government, deep gratitude for involving me in discussions and for assisting me on various occasions.

To the Blockchain Association of Canada and all the people who over the years have helped to educate Canadian individuals, businesses, associations, and government bodies about the potential of blockchain technology. So many people have been closely involved over the years including Philippe Chevry, James Gonzalez, Amber Scott, Manie Eagar, Michael Perklin, Stuart Hoegner, Jason Cassidy, Tracy Leparulo, Reed Holmes, Jeff Coleman, Ethan Wilding, Laurent Pierssens, Adam Aptowitzer, Francis Pouliot, and others; you have all helped get us to where we are now.

To the BAC's founder, crypto legend, and wallet expert Anthony Di Iorio - deep gratitude for your commitment, support, and vision.

To Tanya Woods for all your assistance, support and advice. To Kara Stonehouse for your wisdom, guidance and facilitation superpowers.

To Perianne Boring for her years of dedication and passion in assisting the blockchain and digital asset industry interface with governments and regulators at a global scale with the Chamber of Digital Commerce.

To master strategist Shidan Gouran. To master alchemist Steven Nerayoff. To master crafter Barrymore Richards.

To Chris Reed, Senator Irving Gerstein, and the Senate Banking Trade and Commerce Committee for inviting me to showcase Ottawa's first Bitcoin

Kyle Kemper

ATM, which triggered a long series of fortunate events.

To Joseph David, James Grant, Larry O'Brien, and the CAVIRTEX team for teaching me about exchanges, security, and the nuances of being crypto pioneers.

To Nick Sullivan, Victoria van Eyk, and the ChangeTip team. ChangeTip was one of the most fun and inspiring services I have ever used, and it has shaped who I am and my purpose.
To Yassin Sankar, the professor who put students first, taught us the values of critical thinking, and encouraged us to dream big.

To Malcolm Gladwell, Robert Jordan, Neal Stephenson, Brandon Sanderson, and the many other writers who have deeply inspired me through reading.

To the star-walkers Christopher Hills, Jose Arguelles, Don Miguel Ruiz, & Terence McKenna.

To Satoshi Nakamoto, whoever you are, thank you for your contribution to humanity. Thanks to Bitcoin, we have a choice.

To David Wachsman for being a mentor and partner in bringing the message of the blockchain industry to journalists and media consumers globally.

To Ross Ulbricht, the innovator/creator who built the Silk Road marketplace and is victim of a corrupt and perverse justice system - freeross.org

To Peter Tunney for teaching me that the time is always now, expectations are blueprints for disappointment, that the truth always happens, and for inspiring me to unlock my artist within. GRATTITUDE.

To Lee & Spencer Stein and the Spiral Health team. To Domonique for her drive, love, and generosity. To Elena for her energy, spirit, and artistic contributions to the book.

To my fellow galactivator Amato, whose energy, mindfulness, playfulness, and love for others helped unlock my inner-monkey. To Judd Weiss for his dedication to liberty and for providing me counsel and shelter on many LA nights.

To the Summit crew and Venice family including Joel, Regan, David, Brett, Jeff, Kevin, Leslie, and Langely. Thank you for opening me to Tulum and welcoming me to an incredible community of wizards, warriors, healers, weavers, ambassadors, and star walkers.

To Brock Pierce for his friendship, selflessness, generosity, infinite love, and relentless effort to solve large problems and raise the vibration.

Kyle Kemper

To Wiley Matthews for his love, creativity, magic, and music. To Matt McKibbin for being a great advisor and activator.

To Gerardo Trevino for being a mayan warrior and for building trust boosting solutions with Paybook.com that stand to usher in an era of responsible transparency.

To the masterful Ben Gorlick, Simon Chantry, and Josiah Humphrey for a life-changing week where four souls converged forever.

To the master connector, activator, and general Adil Kassam and the UNIFY.org team; world peace is near. To the Jedi Master Adam Apollo, who through the guardianalliance.academy portal is helping individuals master their mind, body, and spirit.

To the Skywalker Thomas and the incredible Khaliya. To the sub-rosa camp.

To the world-bridging Loretta Joseph, who is doing an incredible service connecting the world of Blockchain to the world of geopolitics. To the Honourable Wayne Caines for his leadership in Bermuda and for showing the world how fast a government can move responsibly. To the colourful humanitarian and impact specialist Jane Thomason.

To my Pier 38 USCG FIR family of Andy, Phyllis, Camille, Juraj, Barry, and Curt and to living in style in San Francisco. To Douglas and Naoko.

To Gary Lachance, interstellar human and the founding father of the Decentralized Dance Party, a movement that is bringing people together through dancing, collaboration, creation, and silliness. To Damian "Damo" Michael for his wisdom, consciousness, integrity, and dedication to the movement.

To Kenn Bosak for his dedication to the vision of crypto and for being an incredible evangelist, educator, and activator:
To Juan Galt, Adam Meister, and all the incredible influencers who are helping discuss and diffuse valuable information across the globe.

To Paul Puey and the Edge Wallet team for their dedication and for building one of the best mobile, multi-currency wallets in the space. For years Paul has been at the forefront of securing digital assets and his contributions to the industry are invaluable.

To ambassador Samir Bandali and the coinpayments team for making all cryptocurrencies acceptable.

To Andrei Poliakov and the Coinberry team, who are making buying and selling crypto simple and accessible in Canada and are laying the foundation for new kind of crypto bank.

To Kelvin and the MeVu.bet team for making an app/platform to make betting decentralized.

Everyone has made a bet; this app is like the digital handshake.

To Pierre Bourque for his friendship, dedication, and for being the pioneer behind Blockchain.Radio.

To Leo Gammar and Jaron Lukasiewicz from Agora.vote who are working on making voting secure, easy, and effective.

To Jason Squire, Marino, and the Slate.io team who are building a decentralized Netflix and Ticketing Platform; media will never be the same.

To Gunnar Lovelace, Seth Taube, Nick Sullivan, and the Good Money team . . . the future of money is good. To the magician, the bard, and the globetrotter know as Bear Kittay and his incredible wife Katiyana. To the incredible Toni Lane of Cultu.re for all her love, dedication, and action. To Brigitte June Huff and Alesha Carlander for their guardianship of the sacred feminine and the white tower.

To Stephan Cesarini and @8BillionDreams for helping people identify, declare, and realize their dreams. To Chris Kantrowitz for your love, respect, sensibility, and silliness.

To "Pine" from the Pineapple Fund for giving away 5000+ bitcoin (~$80M at the time) anonymously towards high-impact projects and people. Deep gratitude.

To Serafin Lion Engel and Dan Hawthorne from DataWallet. They are angels helping the people of the world take back control of their data, secure it, and unlock its value.

My life and this movement are filled with so many incredible people that I would like to highlight, but it is simply not possible. The purpose of this book is not to highlight myself or the factors that have led to the present but to showcase what is possible, what's needed, and how we get there.

A final thank-you is also needed, and it is for you. I genuinely appreciate you offering your valuable time to read/skim this book. I hope you enjoyed it.

W INFINITE LOVE & GRATITUDE

KYLE KEMPER

Made in the USA
Middletown, DE
30 August 2021

47179052R00061